Boo the Pest

Written by Lisa Thompson
Pictures by Luke Jurevicius and Arthur Moody

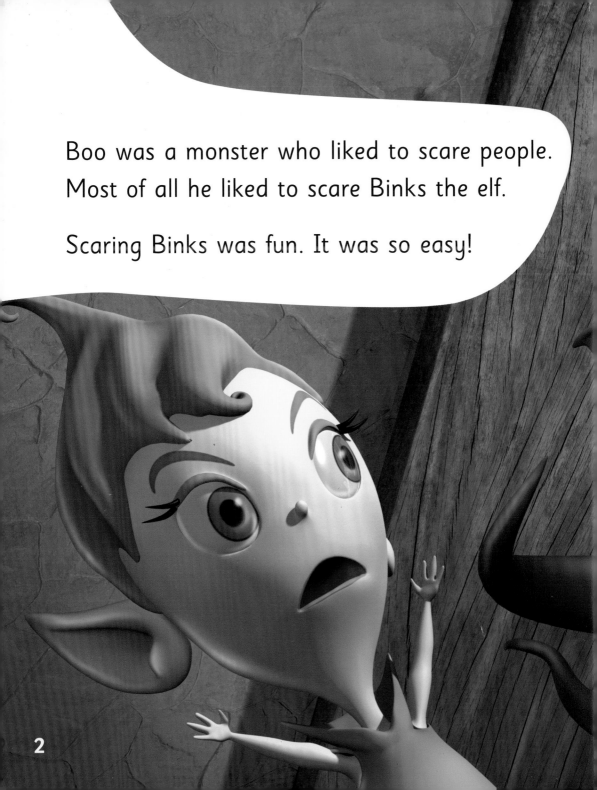

Boo was a monster who liked to scare people. Most of all he liked to scare Binks the elf.

Scaring Binks was fun. It was so easy!

2

3

Soon, Binks got fed up. "That's it!" she said. "How can I get my jobs done, with you scaring me all the time? You're a pest, Boo. Go away!"

"But scaring people is what monsters do," said Boo. "And there are lots of good places to hide in this house."

"Well, I've got jobs to do," said Binks. "You can please yourself!"

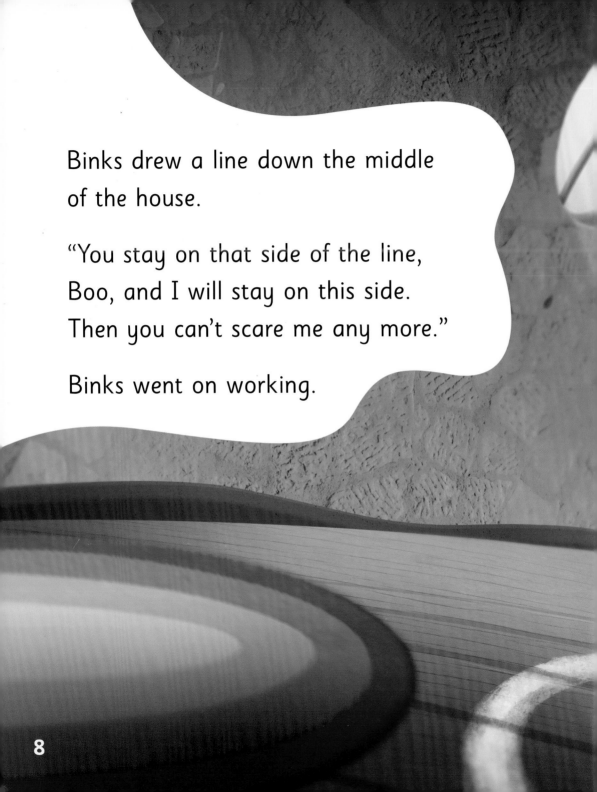

Binks drew a line down the middle
of the house.

"You stay on that side of the line,
Boo, and I will stay on this side.
Then you can't scare me any more."

Binks went on working.

Boo went outside to find someone else to scare. He saw Gog working in the garden.

But Gog was too busy. He didn't even see Boo jumping up and down.

11

So Boo tried to scare Nuggle the spider.
But Nuggle was tired after working on
her web all night. She was too sleepy
to be scared.

Boo got lots of sticky spider web all over
him, but Nuggle just went back to sleep.

Next, Boo tried to scare Dash.
But Boo looked so funny that Dash burst
out laughing. She laughed so hard she
got the hiccups.

15

Boo was fed up. "I can't scare anyone round here," he said.

He curled up in a cupboard and watched Binks working on the other side of the line.

Binks was very busy. Now that Boo was not scaring her, she got on with all her work very quickly.

Soon, the house was sparkling.
All Binks' jobs were done.

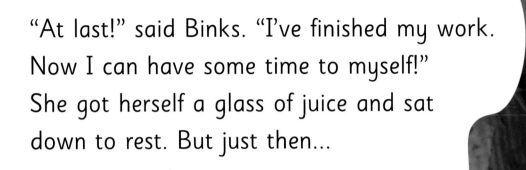

"At last!" said Binks. "I've finished my work.
Now I can have some time to myself!"
She got herself a glass of juice and sat
down to rest. But just then...

"Aaaaaaargh!" Boo leapt out of the cupboard. Binks jumped up in fright. The juice splashed everywhere.

"Boo! You pest!" shouted Binks.

"Sorry, Binks," said Boo. "But I can't help it. Scaring people is just what monsters do."

"I suppose so," said Binks. "And clearing up is just what elves do."

MURDER
& MYSTERIES
– TRUE STORIES IN DEVON –

TOR MARK

First published as *Murders & Mysteries in Devon* by Obelisk Publications, 1996

This 2020 edition published by Tor Mark Ltd,
United Downs Industrial Estate,
Redruth, Cornwall TR16 5HY

www.tormark.co.uk

ISBN 978 0 85025 472 3

AN INTRODUCTION

The stories in this book all have a common theme – a person, usually young, but in one case elderly, dying prematurely at the hands of another. Yes, even a beautiful and quiet county like Devon has had its fair share of murders and mysteries throughout the years.

This book concentrates on the 19th century, a time when the detailed forensic evidence we expect today was unknown – if it had been available then the situations described would probably never have arisen. While the stories have been widely reported elsewhere, this book encourages you to read them with new eyes and perhaps even reach a different, and potentially new, conclusion.

MURDER & MYSTERY
AT HAYNE MANOR

Hayne Manor is a fabulous house set in the heart of glorious Devonshire countryside but only a matter of miles from the River Tamar, the border with Cornwall and not far from the edge of the Dartmoor National Park. The nearest town of any size is Launceston, a place that was to feature in the following amazing saga.

This murder mystery, which was solved by a farmer's vivid dreams, was featured in a book written by G. T. Lowth, published in 1891, the year of the Great Blizzard. No doubt much of the book was written at Hayne, whilst imprisoned by the tremendous drifts of snow that accumulated after 9th March that year, as the Great Blizzard paralysed life in the county for about six weeks. Lowth's book chronicles the story of the manor and what follows is gleaned from Chapter VIII of 'The Home of an Old Family'.

DARTMOOR NATIONAL PARK

THE SILVER HAS GONE –
SO HAS THE PAGE BOY!

It was during the residence of Lord Conway's daughter, Mrs Harris, at Hayne, that a strange and painful incident occurred, to be followed by an even stranger event. It was the custom in those days for a lady of a great house to have in her service a page, who was always at her beck and call, and who was usually seated in the corridor or anteroom near the door of his lady's private apartment. He was always dressed in a smart livery with silver buttons on his jacket and a badge of arms on his collar and sleeves. Mrs Harris had such a page in her service.

The page slept in a closet adjoining the room occupied by the housekeeper, and near the pantry. The page's closet opened into a cloister, consisting of two sides of a quadrangle in the inner court of the mansion, where the offices were situated. The butler slept in a room nearby, also near the pantry, where the household's silver was kept. One morning it became clear the page was missing.

A quantity of the plate had disappeared at the same time, and there was no clue to the robbery. Amongst the most active in endeavouring to find out the means by which the thieves had entered the house and carried off the silver, was the butler. Suspicion had naturally fallen upon him at first, but he was a man of irreproachable character, had been employed by the family for many years and was a great favourite of his master. Furthermore, the butler had been found in the morning by the housekeeper, tied and gagged in the silver room. On being questioned, he could give no account of the affair except that having heard a noise during the night, he had got up and gone to the silver room where he was seized, gagged and tied by the robbers and threatened with death if he uttered a word or tried to leave the room. The only person he had recognized was the page, who had now gone away with the gang.

The housekeeper had also been woken but had been too terrified to raise the alarm. She had been able to untie the butler after the robbers had left. It was conjectured that the page had been made a principal instrument in effecting the robbery, and that he had escaped or been forcibly taken away by the thieves.

There was much distress in the house; whilst Mrs Harris mourned over the loss of her favourite page, Mr Harris caused the most rigid search to be instituted; pawnbrokers and shops of those believed to be receivers of stolen goods at Plymouth and at Exeter were scoured but there was no sign of the stolen articles. Time went on, but both the magistrates and constables continued to draw a blank on the whereabouts of the silver and the missing page.

DREAMS OR NIGHTMARES?

The years went by, and over time, the circumstances became a mystery with no one able to solve the case. Until that is, a great many years passed when, on the occasion of a Court Leet or rent day at Hayne, which was held as usual once a year. It was then that a strange event occurred which appeared connected with the events of the robbery. In those days, the tenants living at a distance in Devon and Cornwall travelled to and slept at Hayne on the night previous to the Court, paid their rent, attended the public dinner on the following day, and on the third day returned home. Two of the tenants, Mr Weare of Tiverton, and Mr Bonifant of Torrington, occupied the same room. During the night, Mr Bonifant awoke suddenly in a great fright, saying that he had had a most appalling dream. He said that a ghostly page boy had appeared to him in his dream and claimed that he had been murdered by the butler and housekeeper who had also stolen the silver!

The apparition said that in the middle of the night he had woken to see the butler and housekeeper packing up the silver into a hamper. When they realised that he was awake they had murdered him on the spot. To ensure secrecy, they had forced his body between the iron bars of the window in the housekeeper's room, carried it to the terrace, then to the Chinese summer house, and buried it behind the wall of that building at the foot of a large yew tree that stood there.

The other farmer, Mr Weare, laughed at the story, judging that the October ale had been too much for Bonifant, and told him to go to sleep again. But when Mr Bonifant dropped off to sleep, Mr Weare had the same dream and, clearly quite terrified, he got up and spent the remainder of the night in an armchair.

During the following day the two farmers, after paying their rent, strolled out into the park, to which they were comparative strangers. They went up to the terrace, and there Bonifant found he recognised the different localities in his dream. This increased the superstitious terror of the farmer. That night the two men again slept in the same room, and again Bonifant had the same dream, repeating the detailed particulars of the robbwery, and of the murder, and this time being beckoned onto the terraces, the Chinese summer house and the yew tree. At this point Weare, previously incredulous, became uncomfortable and the two of them agreed to mention Bonifant's dream to Harris before they left the next morning.

HAYNE MANOR HOUSE

THE BUTLER DID IT!

Mr Harris initially ridiculed the story, but soon realized the strong effect it had had upon the two men. He told them that their minds would be put at rest on the point before they left the house. The first thing Mr Harris did was to write a note to his solicitor at Launceston, requesting him to detain the messenger (the butler) on the understanding that he required an answer back the same day.

After the butler had left on his errand, Mr Harris sent for one of the gardeners and a couple of labourers with spades and pickaxes. Bonifant pointed out the barred windows of the housekeeper's room, between which the body had, allegedly, been forced, the gravel walk at the side of the terrace along which it had been carried to the Chinese summer house, and the yew tree in the ground behind the wall of the building, and at the foot of which the body was buried. Here, he said, was the spot.

Shovels and pickaxes went to work, and for some time there was no result. Mr Harris laughingly told Bonifant that he hoped now he was convinced of the absurdity of his dream about the apparition. But shortly afterwards one of the labourers struck upon, and then turned up, a hard, white metallic substance. Upon examination it was declared to be the silver badge of arms with the family crest, which the page used to wear on his jacket sleeve. The livery buttons were also found, followed by the livery buckles, and at last, the skeleton of the boy was laid bare, huddled up with a few shreds of clothes attached to the silver lace of the livery.

Mr Harris had the bones and relics carefully taken up, carried home and placed in the library before covering them with a sheet. It is easy to imagine the effect of this appalling discovery upon the two farmers and on the whole household. In due time, the butler returned with a letter from the solicitor, and took it into the library. Mr Harris was waiting. He abruptly told the butler that clear and positive evidence had been received of the robbery, the silver and the disappearance of the page. *"The boy was murdered,"* said Mr Harris, *"and was buried under the yew tree, near the Chinese summerhouse."* At this point, he removed the cloth from the bones and relics. The butler was astounded. For a time, he fought against the circumstances. At last, however, he lost his self-possession, fell on his knees and confessed to the robbery and the murder. He said it had been committed precisely and circumstantially in accordance with the dream as related to him by Bonifant.

Following arrest, the events of the dream were proven true by strong collateral evidence, and the butler was committed to prison at once and confined in Launceston Gaol. He was tried and found guilty of the murder and given the sentence of execution. The housekeeper had left the family some years before this, and had gone to live at Exeter, where she had died – with her secret.

DREAMS OR SCHEMES?

It was an amazing story, and many people have tried to explain it. That a man should dream the same thing three times was fairly unusual but you could argue that the second two dreams had already been imprinted onto his mind. But what caused the first dream? The farmer had been in the habit of going to Hayne every year for Court Leet day since the murder and, of course, as everyone connected with Hayne in those days, had talked over the event on each occasion, but nothing had occurred. Even when the incident was fresh and talk abounded everywhere, no vision had come to anyone. But then, when the circumstances were fast fading from people's memories, this had suddenly come in all its detail so remarkably clear and distinct. How many probabilities were there against any one mind conceiving the precise sequence of the facts? If any single person had been likely to weave a fair number of details of the deed, how many probabilities were there against the same individual weaving the long and precise succession of facts that actually took place? No one could give a satisfactory explanation of the strange circumstance.

There were others who said it was the easiest thing in the world to explain, it was not a dream at all – it was an apparition. But this easy explanation did not satisfy some sceptics.

However, there was one man who offered a plausible explanation. He suggested that the housekeeper, who went to Exeter before she died, wanted to ease her conscience. To this end she sent for the farmer Bonifant, an old acquaintance at Hayne and, under the seal of an oath of secrecy, she told him the whole sorry story. When Bonifant went to Hayne on Court Leet day, he walked around the park with Weare and mentally relived the events as told to him. By the time he went to bed his mind was so oppressed with the story of the housekeeper that it all came to him in a dream with a terrible vividness. When he later told of his dream, he would not have been breaking his oath to the housekeeper, merely repeating his own dream.

With such a convincing explanation you might consider this little mystery now solved. However, there is still a loose end… a London-based film company tried to ascertain the basic facts of this story before making a dramatised documentary. They knew that the page boy was a 14 year-old lad called Richard Tarwell, who was murdered by two robbers and the butler, Richard Morris. But when they tried to find proof of the court case and subsequent execution, no records of the incident would come to light, even in Launceston where the case and execution are thought to have taken place. Hasan Shah Films went to great lengths and expense to unearth the truth but could not find a satisfactory conclusion to what appears to have the makings of an excellent ghost story, if only it can be verified!

THE INFAMOUS BABY MURDERER OF TORQUAY

O n the 15th February 1865, at one o'clock in the afternoon, a plasterer called Thomas Milman, who lived at Torre, was strolling along Paignton Road, passing Curtis's Rosery between Torre Abbey turnpike-gate and Torquay station when he made a most horrific discovery. At first, he thought it was just a discarded parcel lying on the snow, but when he folded back the newspaper wrapping, he realised he was holding the body of a baby boy.

TORRE ABBEY

Police enquiries soon led to a knock on the door of Charlotte Winsor, who lived in a cottage in a field near Shiphay Bridge, in the parish of St Marychurch. They knew that she had been minding a child for Mary Jane Harris of Torquay, which she admitted, but said that the mother had removed the child about three weeks previously to place it with an aunt. They tracked down Mary Jane Harris, a servant, at the home of her employer in Warren Road. She confirmed that she had indeed borne a child the previous October, which she had placed in the care of Mrs Winsor, but had since taken it away to live with an aunt. When asked the whereabouts of the child and carer, she replied *"At Peppern, three or four miles the other side of Newton."* Mrs Winsor was asked for the aunt's name which, after some hesitation, she admitted was Harris. Then she paused and said, *"No, not Harris, she is married again – Stevens is her name now."*

When Betsy Stevens, an aunt of Mary Jane Harris, who lived near Heathfield, Chudleigh, was found, she denied taking the child away or even being aware that her niece had a child. The police were sufficiently of a mind to arrest Mary Jane Harris. They also went to Charlotte Winsor's house and searched for evidence. Along with a few items of baby clothes, they discovered a pile of old newspapers, including an old copy of the *Western Times* dated 13th May 1864 – the child's body had been wrapped in a copy of the *Western Times* dated 6th May 1864. Following this, they arrested her as well.

IT WASN'T ME

Once both women were in custody they denied everything. Mary Harris was the more nervous of the two, and kept asking whether she'd hang if they discovered the child's body to be hers. Charlotte Winsor's actions towards her didn't help – she was observed making 'cut-throat' gestures with her finger.

Hoping to prove she had no connection with the dead child, Charlotte Winsor offered to identify the body, as she claimed to clearly remember the boy to have had a flat wart on its foot, which the body of this child didn't. This was backed up by her granddaughter, Selina Pratt, who also said the child had a wart on its foot. However, Mrs Lucy Gibson, who had looked after Mary Harris for about seven weeks after the birth, denied that the child had any such identifying marks. It was Lucy Gibson who had originally suggested that Charlotte Winsor would look after the baby for 3s a week. And, after a baby's body had been found, it was

Lucy Gibson who approached Mary Harris and told her that she had dreamed the child had been murdered by Winsor and that Harris was going to hang for it.

Off the record, Charlotte Winsor told her story to one policeman, which suggested that the mother of the child was quite capable of murdering her own baby. She said that on one occasion she had noticed the baby dribbling and when she tasted the dribble herself, realised it was being fed rat poison. She then left the room and came back to find the baby being held upside down in a pan with water in it. It was at about this point that Mary Jane Harris said her aunt was going to look after the child for 2s a week and took it away from her.

Mr William Stabb, the surgeon who carried out the post-mortem on the child, was unable to determine exactly how it had died. He said it was a well-nourished, healthy-looking infant and on first examination, there was no external appearance to account for death. Even on further examination there was nothing conclusive – the lungs were congested and contained more blood than would have been the case if the infant had died naturally, but there was no appearance of irritation or inflammation about the stomach which would have indicated poison having been administered. The brain was slightly congested but there were no signs of disease there. He came to the conclusion that the child must have died from exposure to cold, but under cross-examination he admitted he had never examined the body of a person who had died from exposure, so he could not swear to it.

THE FIRST TRIAL

The two women appeared in court in March 1865, facing a charge of 'the wilful murder of Thomas Edwin Gibson Harris'. Mary Jane Harris, aged 23, wore a black cloak and a white bonnet of fashionable make, with a sprig of flowers in front. Apparently too languid to sit firmly, she supported herself by resting on her right arm on the side of the dock. Her face was half hidden by her cloak which she pressed against her right cheek. She was of fair complexion, and of prepossessing appearance, but her countenance was overcast, with an expression of deep despondency. Her eyes, generally fixed on the bottom of the dock were rarely raised, and then but for a moment to take a hurried glance at the solemn faces of the jury. She seemed to be weeping, for she frequently wiped her eyes and face with a handkerchief.

The other prisoner, Charlotte Winsor, aged 45, was in the left-hand corner of the dock. Her appearance and demeanour were a contrast to that of Harris. She was dressed in a dark cloth cloak and a black straw hat. Round her neck she wore a red scarf. She boldly faced the court with immovable aspect. Her countenance was sallow, her features long, and her cheeks sunken – perhaps from the anxious time she must have passed awaiting her trial.

The trial excited intense interest. The Court was crowded, and several ladies were present in the High Sheriff's box on the right of the Judge. Mr Isidore Carter appeared for the prosecution on behalf of the Crown.

Eventually, when the Judge summed up the evidence, his address occupied nearly three hours in delivery. He told the jury that they had to decide first of all whether the baby had died a natural death – if not, was it poisoned, drowned or suffocated? Then they had to be satisfied that the child had belonged to Mary Jane Harris. And finally, if the baby was murdered, did either or both of the prisoners in the dock, commit the crime? However, if they were to conclude the baby was Mary Jane Harris's and had been murdered, but were unable to decide who actually committed the deed, then it would be their duty to acquit both prisoners – even if it meant justice hadn't been done.

The Judge also had to remind them not to rely too heavily on the testimony of either against the other, as it would be expected that they would try to shift the blame away from themselves. With respect to Harris' statement to the policeman about her child being with her aunt at Peppern, he remarked that it was clearly a falsehood, yet the jury must not convict her on that alone. The Judge directed the jury that they were not to act upon mere suspicion. The evidence must be such that guilt was brought home to the prisoners, who were entitled to the benefit of any reasonable doubt.

The jury retired to consider their verdict at ten minutes to seven. A few minutes before eleven they were asked if there was any likelihood of their coming to a decision and they said that if they were to agree at all, it would be within the next half-hour.

At ten minutes to twelve, the jury was sent for. They were asked if they agreed upon a verdict. The Foreman said they had not, nor were they likely to agree. He started to say, *"There are eight..."* but the Judge stopped him from giving any particulars. The Judge told the jury that whilst he was unwilling to discharge a jury in criminal cases, if he locked them up for the rest of the night, as it was a Saturday, they would have to stay locked up for the whole of Sunday. Under the circumstances he felt justified in discharging them. The Cathedral clock struck twelve as the Judge retired from the Court.

THE SECOND TRIAL

Four months later, the two women once again stood in court. On being placed at the bar at the commencement of the second trial, the prisoner Harris appeared greatly agitated. She sobbed violently and hid her face in her handkerchief although she had not altered materially in her personal appearance since the last assize; she was neatly dressed in the same apparel. But this time Mr Isidore Carter addressed the Judge with the words, *"My lord, I am instructed on the part of the prosecution, and we do so on grave consideration of the case in all its bearings...to apply to your lordship for leave to call upon the younger prisoner, Mary Jane Harris, as a witness on this occasion on the part of the Crown."* She had turned Queen's evidence. The Judge, after careful consideration, could see no objection to the course being pursued and said that it would be done in the ordinary way – the elder prisoner would take her trial alone, and the other prisoner would be taken as a witness. Mary Jane Harris was then removed from the dock. Quick to take advantage of the situation, her Counsel suggested that, in order to give validity to the proceedings, perhaps Harris should be acquitted at once? The Judge thought she should not.

Charlotte Winsor, the elder prisoner, appeared altered; her look was more haggard, her eyes bore traces of weeping and altogether she did not seem to be so indifferent to the proceedings as on the last occasion. Then she had looked perfectly stoical, but now she paid marked attention to the evidence which particularly implicated her. Speaking on her behalf, Mr Folkard objected to the course about to be taken. He pointed out that the prisoners had already been arraigned before a jury and that jury, he felt, was improperly discharged without arriving at a verdict. Without any disrespect to the Judge before whom the case was tried upon the last occasion, he contended that in point of law the prisoner could not be tried again before another jury. The Judge overruled the objection.

Mr Carter reiterated the facts of the case before Mary Jane Harris was called to give evidence, which she gave with perfect coolness – indeed one would hardly have supposed that she could have related the horrible facts in such a clear manner as she did, although subjected to a severe cross-examination. She told the court that before she had been a servant with Mrs Wansey at Tamar Villas, she had been living with Mrs Gibson, where she gave birth to a fine child with no particular mark upon it. As she was in no position to look after it, she agreed to have the child looked after by Mrs Winsor, whom she had previously met. She placed the child with Mrs Winsor in December and called to see the child four times. Then she discovered that Mrs Winsor was quite capable of 'doing away' with any child for a fee. When asked how she did it, Winsor told her she put her finger to the jugular vein. Winsor had gone on to say she had *"stifled one three weeks old for Elizabeth Sharland, and threw it into Tor Bay, and when it was picked up it was nearly all washed to pieces."* Mrs Winsor went on to complain of killing a baby for her sister, Porey, on the promise of £4. But as she only received £2 she hadn't spoken to her since. Mary Jane Harris asked whether she was afraid, and Winsor replied that she was not at all as she considered, *"it's doing good."* This caused quite a sensation in the court room. Mary Jane Harris explained that Mrs Winsor had said, *"I will help anyone that will never split upon me. I will do whatever lays in my power for your child,"* and continued, *"Give me £5 and I will do away with the child."*

Continuing with her evidence, Mary Jane Harris said that on 9th February she went to Charlotte Winsor's house and saw Selina Pratt, Charlotte's granddaughter, who was playing with the baby. Selina was sent out to buy some candles and after she'd gone, Charlotte Winsor said, *"I didn't do it before you came out, because if you tell on me you must tell on yourself, for one is as bad as the other."* She then took the baby into the bedroom and placed it between the bed ticks. Her husband briefly appeared, and they told him that Harris' aunt was taking the baby. When he went off to Torwood for some pigs-wash, and after the granddaughter had returned and been sent off on another errand, the baby was brought out of the bedroom, dead. Winsor undressed it, took some newspapers out of a box, wrapped the child up and put it into the box. She locked the lid and put the key in her pocket.

Under cross-examination, Mary Jane Harris swore that she did not attempt to poison the child. She said that she always wanted the child to live, although it was true that she stood by and saw it barbarously murdered. She did not put the child there for that purpose. The father of the child, Farmer Nicholls, had allowed her something for the child up to the time she put him with Winsor but not after. He had already provided 3s 6d a week for a previous child by him.

She had known Nicholls seven years and had the two children by the same father. She insisted she had never tried to procure an abortion and that the eldest child was now about six and a half years old.

Mr Stabb stated his opinion that the appearance of the body was consistent with death by suffocation. In his summing up, the Judge pointed out that it was not necessary for the evidence of an 'approver' to be corroborated by untainted evidence in every particular (an approver is one who confesses a crime, and reveals his accomplices). But, having said that, it must be backed up by some hard evidence. He said that by her own words, Mary Jane Harris was clearly an accomplice to a hideous crime and if independent evidence had been available to prove it, without her confession, she now would be in the same position as Charlotte Winsor. He also went on to point out that, in relation to her statement that she wished the child to live, this was patently untrue as she also admitted to standing by and witnessing its murder.

On this occasion, it took the Judge two hours to sum up the case and a mere hour and twenty minutes for the jury to return with a verdict of guilty. The Judge then delivered the solemn announcement that Charlotte Winsor had shown no mercy to the unfortunate child, and so could not expect to meet with any now at the hands of others. She was to be 'taken to a place of public execution, where she would hang by the neck until she was dead'. The prisoner, during the passing of her fearful sentence, sobbed convulsively, and hid her face in her hands. At the conclusion she rose and hurriedly left the dock. All her iron resolution seemed to have completely deserted her, for during the whole of the day she cried and did not once raise her face from out of the handkerchief with which she covered it. The court was crowded during the proceedings and intense excitement prevailed throughout. But whilst the Judge was passing sentence, the stillness was deathlike.

It was reported that there was every probability that Mary Jane Harris would be acquitted. The Home Secretary decided that the proper course to take would be not to grant her a pardon, but to make arrangements for bringing her case before a jury at the next assizes for the county of Devon, when, no evidence being offered on the part of the Crown, she might have the benefit of an acquittal.

Charlotte Winsor also had plenty of time to contemplate her dire situation. Her Counsel, working hard on her behalf, still hadn't given up on his original claim that the second trial was not legal; that when a jury in a capital crime had been discharged without giving a verdict, the proceedings became irregular, and therefore illegal. The Secretary of State postponed the execution until the question of law could be settled by the proper tribunal. A writ of error was brought and decided against Charlotte Winsor by the Court of Queen's Bench. Her execution was fixed for 11th February 1866.

THE EXECUTION THAT NEVER WAS

According to the 'souvenir' broadsheet, published in advance and ready to distribute to spectators hungry for lurid details: *Exeter, Friday – At the usual hour this morning Mrs Winsor expiated her crime on the gallows. Thousands assembled in front of the gaol at a very early hour, and many had walked all night to see the execution. Great commotion prevailed and it was evident that the crowd viewed the execution of a woman as a novelty, while they freely discussed the fiendish nature of the culprit, and expressed their total abhorrence of one who could make a business of murdering illegitimate offsprings. The horrible nature of the woman's crime...shocked the better feelings of humanity, that when culprit and hangman stood side by side a fearful yell rose from the assembled crowd, and the excitement only ceased when the culprit, who struggled but little, ceased to exist.*

Below the writer's own there followed a six-verse rhyming poem recounting the whole sorry story. It finished with the words: *"But justice overtook her, and for these crimes she died. The tempter and the murderess, as you see by these lines, as gone to face their Maker, and to answer for her crimes."*

THE REPRIEVE

Unfortunately for the writer and printer of the broadsheet, the Home Secretary had granted a respite; the reprieve reached Exeter on the Saturday. The executioner, Calcraft, arrived in Exeter by the 3.30pm train, remained all night, before returning to London on the 1.30pm train the next day. It was, however, true that as the news reached Exeter late, it was prevented from extending to the adjoining villages; in consequence, a very large number of persons flocked into the city on Monday morning to witness the execution. On 11th May, the Home Secretary announced that he had determined, under all the circumstances of the case, to recommend that the capital sentence passed on Charlotte Winsor should be commuted to penal servitude for life.

Today, anyone who has heard of Charlotte Winsor will know her as the 'Infamous Baby Murderer'. If she was capable of what she was accused, then she was very lucky indeed to escape the hangman's noose on a legal technicality. But it should be remembered that she was found guilty on the evidence of Mary Jane Harris, who rather than take a gamble on being found not guilty on the second trial, preferred to turn 'Queen's evidence' in order to avoid being hanged herself.

THE MAN THEY COULDN'T HANG

Anybody who has lived in Devon for any significant amount of time may have heard of the amazing story of John Lee and will know that he too cheated the hangman's noose. In this case, the murderer came close to death no less than three times. He acquired the nickname 'Babbacombe' Lee, for that is where horrific events were to unfold, in a house called *The Glen*.

BABBACOMBE BAY, TORQUAY

ROYAL RELATIONS?

Emma Keyse was affluent, with good connections. Many writers have claimed she was once a 'Maid of Honour' to Queen Victoria but it was actually her mother who had the royal connections and may even have been a governess to the young Princess Victoria. There is a belief that Henry VIII had a son by Mary Boleyn, sister of the fateful Anne, who was subsequently married her off to a Colonel named Keyse who was given a large acreage of land round Hatherleigh, as well as Manor House. Emma Keyse is thought to be the cousin of the last in the line. She had assembled her own retinue which included three women and one man. The latter was John Lee, who hailed from Abbotskerswell, a small but pretty village on the outskirts of Newton Abbot. He first went to work at *The Glen* in 1879, at the young age of 14 or 15.

Whilst at *The Glen* he was at the beck and call of Miss Keyse. From time to time his errands took him out of the house and whenever he could, he engaged local fishermen and sailors in conversation. One might assume from this that these old seadog characters would have been an influence on this highly impressionable young man, for the following year saw him leave the service of Miss Keyse in order to join the Navy.

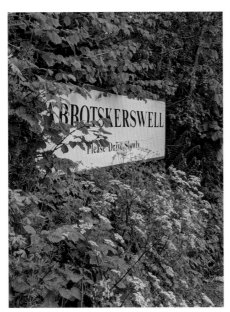 

ABBOTSKERSWELL

FLUCTUATING FORTUNES

Fate is a fickle friend, for the circumstances which were to shape young John Lee's life took an initial turn for the worse, when he caught pneumonia and was obliged to leave the Navy. He had enjoyed the life and felt bitter about being invalided out of the service. His adjustment was difficult with three jobs in as many weeks. He first went to the Yacht Club Hotel at Kingswear, then became a porter at Torre Station in Torquay but this wasn't 'the ticket' for him either.

Finally, he found his way into the employment of Colonel Brownlow as his footman, thanks to a recommendation from Emma Keyse. When the Colonel had to go away for a while, he left Lee in charge of his large house; alas during this time some of the Colonel's silver items found their way down to a local pawn shop. John Lee's rather poor excuse for pawning the valuable silverware was that he had a friend who was off to Australia and needed financial assistance. The Judge was less benevolent and sentenced John to six months imprisonment, this being served in the latter half of 1883 at Exeter Prison.

On John's behalf, his half-sister, Elizabeth Harris, persuaded Emma Keyse to re-employ him in his old post. She had replaced John's other sister, Amelia, as Emma's cook. She also knew that the old lady had something of a soft spot for John Lee, as she had watched him grow into manhood and felt some responsibility towards him. Thus reinstated at *The Glen*, things were beginning to look up for him again as he worked hard in those first few months after his return. He found himself a young lady, Katie Farmer, and started courting seriously. However, the euphoria of having left prison and making a new start eventually began to wear off and Lee became dissatisfied with his life. Miss Keyse tried to help him find other work more suited to him but without success. His response, which Lee himself denied, was not always a mild mannered one and there were suggestions that Lee reacted in a most aggressive manner towards his kindly boss.

Perhaps the limited fetching and carrying nature of his position was getting to him, for he worked in a household which comprised three other staff. In addition to his half-sister there were the Neck sisters, Jane and Eliza, who had worked for Miss Keyse for several decades. The claustrophobic effect made John Lee feel that there was more to life than being cooped up with three elderly ladies and a half-sister. His mind turned towards a career in the army. Miss Keyse, potentially in a frame of mind that thought it may be as well to move him along the road out of *The Glen*, promised to pull a few strings. For such a respectable lady with the right connections, there were few doors closed to her when she needed something.

MURDER MOST FOUL

After a typical November day in the life of the Keyse household, certain daily rituals were enacted as they had always been. At ten o'clock, on the night of the 14th November 1884, the staff prepared to say evening prayers, except for Elizabeth Harris, who had gone to bed much earlier feeling unwell. The prayers were led, as always, by Miss Keyse and lasted about a quarter of an hour. John Lee turned in shortly afterwards, but Miss Keyse was something of a night owl and never went to bed until the small hours. These routine events were a prelude to a terrible tragedy.

That night was the last time Miss Keyse was seen alive, for somebody struck her a violent blow on the head, cut her throat and then set fire to her body and the house. Elizabeth Harris was the first on the scene, between 3 and 4am She raised the alarm by waking the Necks, who had been asleep upstairs. Hearing the commotion, John Lee appeared and helped them search the smoke-filled rooms for Miss Keyse. The smoke was so thick that he broke a window to let it out. As he did so he cut his arm, blood flowing freely from the wound. However, his action had the desired effect of dispelling some of the smoke. At the same time as Elizabeth entered the room, John Lee spun around to see the body of Miss Keyse lying prostrate on the floor. It was obvious that a heinous crime had been committed.

After helping the Necks downstairs, John Lee and Jane Neck first roused a local fisherman, called Stiggins, who lived in a cottage, also owned by Miss Keyse, by the beach. John was then immediately despatched to summon help from the Landlord, Mr Gaskin, at the nearby Cary Arms, a pub that is still there to this day. He and Mr Gaskin moved Miss Keyse's body out of the house. Attempts were made to put out the fire, John Lee playing his part by taking an axe, from an outside shed, to chop out a beam that was causing problems with fire-fighting. Whilst those involved in this crisis struggled with the fire, the police were on their way.

In cases like this, the fundamental task of any detective investigating the scene is to determine whether this was a domestic killing or whether an outsider was involved. An inspection of all the external doors and windows suggested that the guilty person had been a resident at *The Glen*. Shortly afterwards, John Lee was charged with the murder of Miss Keyse – in the hall, with an axe. Lee soon realized that he was the prime suspect. He had also provided, albeit unwittingly, further clues, even damning evidence, by spreading his blood around after breaking the window. In the days before forensic science, there was no way of identifying whose blood was on his hands.

The police let him visit the doctor by himself, but it did not stand him in good stead that he innocently returned to the house rather than taking the opportunity to escape. In addition to this the police found near John Lee's sleeping quarters, the adapted pantry, several bloodstained items including the hatchet, a knife, and a pair of bloodstained trousers that reeked of paraffin.

At Torquay Police Station the formalities were conducted at pace, with John Henry George Lee being charged with the murder of his employer, Miss Emma Keyse.

To compound Lee's problems, Emma Keyse had been a pillar of society; she was well-known and highly respected, and her death had appalled the people of Torquay. Naturally, feelings about the murder ran high. Locals viewed it as a foregone conclusion that Lee committed the murder and he became a hated man.

The Inquest was held at the Town Hall in St Marychurch on 28th November. The verdict was no surprise – 'Wilful murder' – and John Lee was named as the perpetrator of this crime.

There was nothing new about Lee's next stop as he was familiar with Exeter Prison, having spent time there the previous year. It must have been a sober Christmas for him as he awaited trial. Like the majority of men in this situation, Lee had protested his innocence long and loud but he was enough of a realist to know that even if *he* knew the truth, it was going to be little more than a formality to find him guilty of the charge. He was also very aware of the implication of such a verdict, but he remained surprisingly calm. Realistically, there was little he could do about his predicament.

THE TRIAL

The trial date was set for the Devon Assizes at Exeter on Monday 2nd February 1885. There was a tremendous interest in the trial. To get passes for it was difficult, there being many more hundreds of would-be spectators than room would permit in the court. Lee's mother turned up without a pass and only managed to get in to see her son's trial after a lot of fuss following a heated argument with court officials.

John Lee's journey through the incessant rain from the prison to the court was a lot longer than it would have been normally, for the Governor was anxious to avoid any street riots. This being achieved, with a round-about route, Lee was held in custody in a cell, the size of a cupboard, below the court room, until everyone had been assembled ready for the start of proceedings. On the Saturday afternoon Lee discovered that his solicitor, Reginald Gwynne Templer, had been taken ill, and his brother, Charles, was taking over the case. He assured him that there was nothing to worry about and that Lee would not have to say anything in order to be set free.

The case lasted three days. The ordeal for John Lee was a difficult one because he was a simple country lad who had never even seen a Judge before, his last case having been presided over by magistrates. In even the most straightforward case the exchange of words, the repetition, and the legal terminology could lead to confusion. John Lee sat through it albeit without understanding much of the proceedings. Throughout the trial, which he knew was a life or death affair, John Lee, having made a plea of 'not guilty', showed little interest in what was going on or being said.

The jury did not take long to deliberate on their verdict for there was no alternative but to record a 'guilty' judgment. It came as no real surprise to John Lee as he heard this confirmed. This was followed by the pronouncement of the death sentence, that of by 'being hanged by the neck.'

As John Lee was about to leave the court he spoke out, addressing the Judge with this statement: *"The reason why I am so calm is that I trust in the Lord, and He knows I am innocent!"*

HANGING ABOUT

Lee's belief did not fade in the days that followed the trial as he sat in the condemned cell awaiting his pending execution. There were a few minor compensations, not least the bed being more comfortable than was the norm for the rest of the prisoners at the gaol. The diet was also more flexible, there being a degree of choice which was not available to the rest of the inmates. However, there were drawbacks as Lee was never left unattended, with two warders with him night and day. Each pair worked twelve-hour shifts. By night one slept whilst the other sat in a chair, these two taking turns at their custodial duties.

The Governor appeared a few days after John Lee had arrived to inform him that the execution was scheduled to take place on 23rd February. Lee's reaction was one of partial relief for he wanted to know where he stood in order to come to terms with the situation.

He wrote letters to his mother and sister, in which he appeared calm and resigned to the inevitable. To his mother, he wrote, *"I do not know whenever I was happier than I am now, because I know where I am going to... What does it matter about a few years in this world? We must all leave it some time."* After signing the letter *"From your affectionate son, J. H. Lee"* he wrote, *"N.B. – The day is fixed for the 23rd of this month. Good-bye."*

To his sister, Amelia, he said, *"...it is hard to be punished when one knows that he did not do it, but I will trust in the Lord and ask Him to give me strength to bear it all. This world's punishment it is nothing after all for a better home above...there is no doubt the truth will come out after I am dead. It must be some very hard-hearted persons for to let me die for nothing. All the witnesses will and must appear before our Saviour for what they have said against me and to answer for my life, they little think of it now, but the time will soon come for them, and I hope they will be prepared to meet our Saviour. I thank God I am not blind so as not to know what I have seen and what I have done. They have not told six words truth, that is, the servants and that lovely step-sister who carries her character with her."* He signed this letter *"From your affectionate brother, who is dead to the world."*

A DRAMATIC 'EXECUTION'

The dreaded day of execution arrived. It was an early start for John Lee, waking at 6.30am to find the prison chaplain in his cell with him. However, the man of the cloth stepped outside in order to allow John Lee to get dressed in semi-privacy. John had experienced another of his deep sleeps, this filled with the most incredible dream. He had to tell his two warders, whom he had come to look on as friends, or the nearest he would get in such dire circumstances. He told them that he had been taken to the scaffold, that three times the bolt had been drawn on the trap door but three times had failed. They listened but did not respond. One of those men was James Milford, an Exeter man.

The chaplain, Mr Pitkin, came in to pray with John. He tried to get a confession out of Lee but none was forthcoming. The time passed on towards the appointed hour of execution – 8am. As the hour struck, the chaplain, the Governor (Mr Cowtan) and the hangman, James Berry, stepped into the condemned's cell. Both shook hands with Lee, the hangman telling Lee that he had his job to do. He was a short man who was scientific in his approach to dispensing with his victims. Berry placed various straps around Lee's person. The assembled group, which now included warders, an under sheriff and others, made a small procession. This was to lead to the scaffold but as Lee prepared to meet his Maker with the words of the burial service in his ears, he started to take notice of his surroundings. These he couldn't have seen before, but they were so familiar to him. Almost immediately he realised that what confronted him was exactly the same scene as he had dreamed the night before! He had not been taken along the fatal route before.

Outside the prison a crowd had gathered just as they did for every execution. In the past, executions were a public affair with thousands coming to watch. At least Lee was to be spared this. The press, who always wrote in such great detail in those days, were also there in force. Many had already written up the execution as a fait accompli, but perhaps they should have held their pen-power back for just a while longer for what was about to happen, or not happen, was a sensational story for journalists.

The procession continued slowly onwards towards the scaffold, the grim bell tolling, this time for John Lee. The group crossed a garden near the Governor's house and approached a low wooden shed with its big doors wide open. The large prison van that it normally housed had been moved out so that the execution could take place. Lee saw the rope that was to hang him. He was puzzled for he had imagined the sort of gibbet where a fall through the air would result in the victim's demise. How, on earth, would he get onto the roof of the shed? It then dawned on him, for the first time, that there would be a trap door – just like in his dream. The hangman led John Lee to a point on the trap door directly beneath the beam from which the hangman's noose dangled. The hangman tied a belt around Lee's ankles whilst parts of his life flashed through his mind. Memories of Abbotskerswell days filled a few of those tense seconds. James Berry then pulled a bag-like item over Lee's head. The rope came next, first quite loose but then tightened right up Lee's throat almost to his ear. The hangman gave Lee one last opportunity to say anything, which he declined. The massive bolt which triggered the trap door mechanism was pulled, but as it didn't work as expected. The executioner stamped on the trap in a bid to force it open and with this increased weight it opened a few inches.

What should have been a routine execution turned into an ordeal for Lee, because for about five or six minutes he stood on the drop whilst the warders joined in and jumped up and down in order to force the trap door open. When the trap door remained steadfastly shut, Lee was eventually taken off and placed in an adjacent storeroom.

For several frantic minutes the warders and other prison personnel struggled with the bolt. They managed to get it to work, testing it several times and Lee, not that far away, could hear the trap door dropping open. Imagine the terror that he must have endured. James Berry was not an insensitive man and muttered what may be construed as an apology to Lee for what had happened. However, Berry still had his job to do and Lee was once more escorted back to the gallows. Some of the spectators had found the experience an unbearable one to witness and turned their heads away, preferring not to see the outcome. Again, the same procedures were followed. The bolt was pulled and Lee plunged suddenly but only a few inches. Warders stamped on the trap door but it was to no avail. Lee was requested to step backwards off the device with all the apparel for the execution still in harness around his neck. Inevitably in such an uncomfortable position he choked and gasped for.

There was probably more attention given to the scaffold than the intended victim. The bolt was tried again and again. It worked well. Perhaps the planks had swollen through damp like doors often do. A carpenter gave them some attention by passing a saw through the gaps. After another five minutes Lee was placed on the trap door for a third time. The same scenario followed with Lee left on his toes as the doors moved just a few inches. The warders gave one last cursory bout of stamping on them, but they wouldn't budge.

Lee was taken off for a third time, the belt around his legs was removed. He was in a state of distress having been put through all sorts of tortures. He was also suffering from a lack of air as the hood that he wore had cut off most of his air supply. Slowly John Lee regained his breathing and began to calm down a little. Once more Berry appeared, this time with tears in his eyes. He started to unshackle Lee as the condemned man was finding it hard to bear the suspense and the nerve-breaking strain.

FOR WHOM THE BELL TOLLS

The chaplain told John Lee that he believed that the laws of the country dictated that he could not be put on the scaffold again. Lee's dream had come true! It later transpired that Lee's mother, at home in Abbotskerswell and in a very distressed state, had also had a similar dream, although in her dream, the rope snapped. In addition to this there had been ghostly knocking emanating from an adjacent, empty room.

There was even the compensation for Lee of an extra breakfast. The doctor checked him over and told him that he could have anything he wanted. Despite his appetite being revived, Lee asked if he could defer the breakfast treat until the next day. In the meantime, the prison bell tolled its death knell; the ringer had been instructed to carry on ringing until the flag was hoisted to signal the completion of the execution. This, of course, never came.

However, far from being elated, Lee knew that the Home Secretary would have to sanction any reprieve or respite and that would take some time to establish.

Lee's roller-coaster of emotion was later given a further ride when, after a dinner of steak and port wine, he was taken to the exercise yard. Here he saw a fresh mound of earth, which was the soil removed from the ground where his grave, plot number 8, had been dug. This remained open for the next few days but was eventually filled-in before Lee had the chance to see it again. As around 10pm that evening, Mr Cowtan appeared in Lee's cell to inform him that he had been given a period of respite. It was nearly a month before Her Majesty commuted the capital sentence to penal servitude for life, this being later specified as 20 years. However, Lee did 22 long years, having been held at five different prisons, mostly at Portland.

On a really clear day it's possible to see all the way across Lyme Bay from Portland to Babbacombe, the venue of the cause of Lee's incarceration; in this instance, a case of so near but yet, so far.

OVERLOOKING THE BEACH AND CLIFFS AT BEER, IN LYME BAY, DEVON

WHO DUNNIT?

Lee never confessed to murder, but he did say that he deserved hanging for not telling all he knew about the matter. Anyone who thinks he 'got away with murder' or profited in some way from his notoriety should read his own account of what prison life was like for him; he found it a living hell and believed death might even have been preferable. Those are the facts behind his story but, once again, it throws up many questions. Was there more to the story in that it wasn't just the way things worked out? John Lee had every faith in his own innocence and that he would not be punished by God. We may be sceptical about this, but he wasn't. Or did he know more than he let on and his confidence was backed by the certainty that he wasn't going to hang? Was his 'dream' a true premonition or was it a carefully prepared story designed to add weight to the events which were to follow?

There are many theories that go back to the root cause of John Lee's predicament. Was he guilty of the murder of Emma Keyse? There have been plenty of people keen to stress that he wasn't and that he merely took responsibility for someone else's crime. But who could have done it and why? Emma Keyse was an elderly with no known enemies. But she was reputed to have had confrontations with local fishermen, and possibly smugglers. She had been found downstairs but why was she there? Did someone enter the house, commit murder and then escape without waking the deeply sleeping Lee? Surely if John Lee had murdered her, he would probably have done so upstairs where the old lady slept. And why did he not make good his escape? He must have realised that being the only man in the house would make him the prime suspect.

Did Emma Keyse find somebody she knew downstairs? We can rule out the elderly Neck sisters from the equation. However, Elizabeth Harris, the cook and John Lee's unmarried half-sister, is less easy to dismiss. She was just three-months pregnant in an age when this was a deep disgrace. She had gone to bed at teatime on the night of the murder. According to John Lee she had access to her room by both the front door and the back door – had she been in her room the whole time? What if the old lady had discovered her and her lover together in the wee small hours and the lover had panicked and thought to 'shut her up'. Even if her lover hadn't been present, why did everyone assume it had to be a man who committed the murder?

Elizabeth Harris was about 30 years old and had been a cook for many years, so probably had a few muscles of her own. Why did no one seem to question her ability to swing an axe into the older lady's skull? Harris was the one who alerted the household to the fire. Her evidence was crucial in John Lee's conviction and could have been a way of saving her own skin, and that of her secret lover. Her family disowned her after the trial and John Lee is also thought to have made great efforts to follow-up 'the cook's deathbed confession' – the existence of which was strongly denied by the Home Secretary. It has also been said that John Lee wrote to his other sister, Amelia, and said *"You must forgive Lizzie, I do ...it is my fault I ought to have opened my mouth before."* The plot is made more intriguing by the notion that Miss Keyse's solicitor was Mr Isidore Carter, the very same solicitor who had, 20 years earlier, been involved in the case of the infamous baby killer, Charlotte Winsor. Some people have been known and suggested that Mary Jane Harris was John Lee's mother – but the coincidences make your head reel! John Lee's mother was also a Mary Harris before she married Mr Lee, which was where his half-sister Elizabeth fitted into the picture. Mary Jane Harris admitted having an older child. John Lee is said to have been born in August 1864, whilst Mary Jane Harris's son, Thomas was born in October 1864. If Mary Jane Harris did witness her child being murdered by Charlotte Winsor, then he clearly could not be John Lee. But Harris and Winsor's original defence was that the child was alive and living with an aunt. The jury had been directed to find them guilty of murder only after they were sure the baby was Harris'. As we know, the jury didn't reach a verdict. It was only at the retrial that Harris changed her story firmly implicating Charlotte Winsor. Many years ago, it was reported that Carter had always upheld privately that John Lee was the son of Mary Jane Harris.

What seems very likely is that the two women, Mary Jane Harris and Mary (née Harris) Lee, were actually cousins. When questioned by the police, Mary Jane Harris claimed that her baby had gone to live with her aunt, Betsy Stevens at Peppern, three or four miles the other side of Newton. At that time, Elizabeth Harris was being raised by her maternal grandmother, Bessie, whose second husband, William Stevens owned Pepperdon Farm, Kingsteignton. Knowing her own baby to be dead, it is posisble Mary Jane Harris invented a story based on the facts of her cousin's situation.

There have been many knowing nods and winks about the 'real' murderer and many stories of influential people seeing to it that Lee was the scapegoat who really didn't deserve to die. Probably the best conspiracy theory is that John Lee didn't actually deliver the fatal blow personally but was 'on the scene' so would therefore have been charged with murder anyway. Given the circumstances of a wealthy, well-educated and well-known gentleman being responsible, he might well have made the suggestion that if John Lee was to take the blame, this gentleman would be in a position to use his wealth and influence to pay for the defence and, ultimately, make sure Lee didn't hang. And as we all know – John Lee did not hang.

Elizabeth Harris gave birth to a daughter in a Newton Abbot workhouse and never had any further contact with her family. She always refused to name the father of her child and clearly received no support from him so he might well have been dead. Many theories have been put forward over why the gallows didn't work. A gentleman who lived in Howell Road, growing up opposite the prison, says that his father knew how the scaffold had been cleverly constructed so that the trap door would fail to operate when the chaplain stood immediately in front of the condemned man. This clearly worked well as when the prisoner was removed, and the chaplain stood back, the trap door worked perfectly. It is a fact that throughout history, prisons have been more comfortable for prisoners with money or influence. It is not beyond belief that either or both could have contrived to ensure that John Lee did not hang.

The longer you live and the more you see makes you appreciate that there aren't many cases of black or white, just shades of grey. The possible twists in this crime would have made a mystery writer proud.

THE AFTERMATH

The Glen was put up for sale but with no one interested in buying the charming cottage, it was demolished in 1894. The cottage itself stood close to where the public conveniences are located. It's a beautiful place to be on a fine, sunny morning. But what of John Lee? As far as is known, he didn't transgress again. He went home to his widowed mother in Abbotskerswell and wrote his autobiography. He married Jessie Bullied, a Newton Abbot woman, and fathered two daughters, probably in the North East of England. He was seen in London in late 1911, shortly before his solo emigration, where his wife claimed parish relief for herself and her two children the following year.

Opinions are divided as to where Lee's travels took him after that. Many people believe that he went to Canada at that time to start a new life as a gold prospector. It has also been suggested that his last years were spent in the workhouse at Tavistock, on the edge of Dartmoor, where he is purported to have died. According to other accounts he is supposed to have died in Milwaukee in 1933, whilst it's been suggested that he cheated death in London, a decade later, when he was pulled from a burning building. If you throw in another rumoured Lee death in Australia, you will have a man who appears to have more lives than a cat and more deaths than is normally regarded as being conducive to good health.

His entire life seems to have been shrouded in mystery. And such a web of intrigue hasn't gone unnoticed by film makers and record producers. A silent film of John Lee's life story was released in 1917, the premier taking place in Cardiff. Some 50,000 people flocked to see it. When it was shown in Newton Abbot many of his relations travelled from Abbotskerswell to see it but what they thought of it is not known. The folk-rock group 'Fairport Convention' wrote an entire album about John 'Babbacombe' Lee's story in the 1970s.

A MISCARRIAGE
OF JUSTICE

If a vestige of sympathy has been for John Lee's plight in serving over 20 years in prison for a crime he claimed he did not commit, now is the time to spare some for poor old Edmund Galley, also betrayed by an Elizabeth Harris, but not, the same girl. Not only did Edmund Galley proclaim his own innocence, he was backed up by his 'partner in crime', the witnesses, who were people as far afield as Kent, the House of Commons, in fact everyone except the Home Secretary! Another similarity with John Lee is that Edmund Galley escaped the hangman's noose – by just one week. This was more than just lucky for him – had he been found guilty one week earlier, he would have been hanged and a posthumous pardon isn't quite the same thing.

HIGHWAY ROBBERY

The story appears to start on 16th July 1835, when a popular, well-respected farmer called Jonathan May was brutally attacked and robbed whilst he was returning from a very successful day at the Moretonhampstead Fair. In fact, the story really starts the previous year when one of his workers, George Avery, was fired on the spot for helping himself to the farmer's logs. George Avery was also present at the Fair that day in 1835, accompanied by his lady friend, Elizabeth Harris.

Although the paths of the two men do not appear to have crossed that day, George Avery behaved rather suspiciously, establishing an alibi by continually asking people the time even though there was a clock clearly visible on the wall. In any case, he went to bed at 10pm and therefore he could not have been lying in wait at the one-milestone point in order to ambush and kill Jonathan May, who was dragged from his horse, hit over the head and robbed of his watch and loaded wallet. Such was the speed and power of the 'underground telegraph', that it was being reported the following day that two murderers had fought for the spoils of the robbery and one had taken the lot.

Various people were suspected and many arrested, including George Avery and Elizabeth Harris. Gradually everyone was discharged apart from Avery, a man called Carpenter (the evidence against whom was that he'd been squirted with calf's blood as a joke and also carried a stick similar to that used for the attack), and a young man called Pardew, who had no evidence against him except having been seen in Carpenter's company and was regarded as of 'bad character'. Eventually all three had to be released and there the story might well have ended.

SUSPECTS APPREHENDED

During the summer of the following year, the Chaplain of Dorchester Gaol wrote to Mr Moses Woolland Harvey, a Moretonhampstead solicitor who had taken a great interest in the case as he'd been a personal friend of the victim. The Chaplain informed Harvey that one of their prisoners, known as 'Oliver', had been overheard boasting about robbing a Devonshire farmer. 'Oliver' was actually a nickname – he was also known as Buckingham Joe – but his real name was Joseph Infield. He was nearly 22 years of age, five feet seven and a half inches in height and strongly built. He was born at West End, a hamlet in Buckinghamshire where his mother still resided, his father having died a few weeks before the previous Christmas.

Mr Harvey immediately rushed off to Dorchester and, with the help of the Dorset police, searched Infield's lodgings and found the watch and other articles which had belonged to Mr May. Infield was awaiting transportation for life, having been convicted on three indictments for highway robbery at Dorchester. He was whisked back to Exeter County Prison and faced identification from half a dozen Moretonhampstead folk. They all swore positively that he had been at the Fair with an accomplice.

So far so good. Where does the injustice of the case come into play you might ask. Whilst all this was going on there was a young man cooling his heels in Cold Bath Fields Prison in London, charged with vagrancy. His real name was Edmund Galley but occasionally he went under the nickname 'Turpin'. Coincidentally, 'Oliver's' accomplice was also called Turpin. The witnesses who had identified 'Oliver' were ready to identify Turpin, so Edmund Galley was sent to Exeter for a positive identification. Whereas everyone had been unanimous in 'Oliver's' identification, there was some doubt as to Turpin's. One lady actually swore that he definitely was not the accomplice. She said the other man had been good looking and taller with a front tooth missing. Her evidence was dismissed by the Judge.

Throughout this time, a reward of £100 and a pardon had been offered to anyone giving information leading to the conviction of the murderers. George Avery and Elizabeth Harris were awaiting transportation to Australia, he having been convicted of highway robbery at Alphington, and she of larceny. One night, Elizabeth Harris suddenly had a terrible dream; she claimed the murdered farmer, Jonathan May, came to her and said if she didn't tell what she knew then he would murder her.

TAVISTOCK

Elizabeth Harris gave evidence that having had an argument with Avery, she had spotted 'Oliver' and 'Turpin' and, suspecting them of being up to no good, had followed them as they left town. She had hidden behind a hedge as she heard the sound of blows and a scuffle. She had no difficulty in identifying 'Oliver', but with a little encouragement, and allowing for the passage of time, taking into account his appearance had altered somewhat, she identified Galley as 'Turpin'.

ABSENCE IS NO EXCUSE

The trial commenced in July 1836, with Mr Justice Williams taking the crown-court. It might be a good moment to point out that Mr Justice Williams was already notorious from the trial of the Tolpuddle Martyrs. Joseph Infield was well defended, Edmund Galley was not. The Judge did not help – although he warned the jury not to accept Harris's testimony without corroboration, he failed to distinguish the weight of the case against 'Oliver' from the weight of the case against Galley. He also misread a name, giving the clear impression that Galley must have been in Moretonhampstead at the time. Unfortunately, noone interrupted the Judge to put the fact straight as they took it for granted the jury would see through the lack of evidence and not convict Galley anyway. Alas, 12 tired and weary jurymen wanted to go home and they took all of ten minutes to declare both prisoners 'guilty'.

Galley had been offered the chance to cross examine the witnesses but as he pointed out, he didn't know the town, or its people, so wouldn't know what to ask them. He did however proclaim his absolute innocence, even though he agreed that anyone who had committed the crime should pay the ultimate price. Joseph Infield did at least try to put matters to right. He swore before God that this person was not 'Turpin', and that he had never set eyes on him before in his life. He reiterated the fact that 'Turpin' was taller and much better looking.

The Judge decided that both men were guilty, and nothing was going to sway him from his verdict. Fortunately for Galley his trial had not taken place a week earlier when the law at that point required that sentence should be carried out within 48 hours of conviction.

It took a couple of days for Edmund Galley to gather his senses together sufficiently to recall that he had been at Dartford Fair, in Kent, on the same day as the Moretonhampstead Fair had taken place. He remembered a few minor incidents which other people might also recall so letters were sent on his behalf to verify his statements. The breakthrough came when at least three people could be found who remembered Galley being at the Fair. Many eminent people pursued the new evidence, and all came to the same conclusion that it was genuine. This was despite a rather mean trick by the authorities, who sent Galley to the 'Ganymede Hulk', where they shaved his head and mingled him with the other prisoners. Not only did his witnesses pick him out, they called his name and approached with such confidence that no one could doubt their authenticity. With his alibi firmly established, the Home Office was approached, and Galley was reprieved. The respite was brief, though, because Mr Justice Williams was consulted by the Home Secretary and he insisted that Galley had had a fair trial and that the evidence against him was conclusive.

In the meantime, 'Buckingham Joe', alias 'Oliver', was preparing to meet his date with destiny on 12th August 1836, over the entrance to the Exeter County Gaol. Even at this late stage, knowing that his life was to end shortly, he attempted to clear Galley's name. He even named the real 'Turpin' as 'Longley'. But, strangely, even though the magistrates at Bath had made known that they had remanded a man called Longley, who fitted the right description, no attempt was ever made by the Devonshire authorities to pursue the matter.

THE RED HANDKERCHIEF

The day of execution arrived. Crowds gathered from all quarters, particularly the West and North, as it was market day. A hoaxer spread the word that the execution was to take place at eight o'clock, but the huge crowd dispersed a little when it was discovered to be later. At 12.15 'Oliver' took leave of the Governor and joined the procession down the avenue. He walked erect and with a firm step, being dressed as at his trial in a blue coat, black waistcoat, and cassimere breeches, blue worsted stockings and short boots. He looked pale and, seeing the daughter of an officer of the prison in tears, his own eyes filled, but he checked himself from further giving way. His hair was neatly combed to one side, and he carried a red cotton handkerchief in his right hand.

The executioner removed his neckerchief and bared his neck, he was pinioned, and heavy irons were appended to his right leg. He then shook hands with the officers of the prison, thanked them indicated that he was ready. Bound as his arms were, and ironed, he could not move up the remaining narrow steps freely, yet still he stepped firmly, and took his station on the platform, when the rope was placed around his neck, and fastened to the fatal beam.

At this time the scene outside was extraordinary; it was one of the finest of summer days, and a huge crowd had gathered, far exceeding the usual numbers.

The Rev Vidal paused whist reciting the final service and asked the prisoner if he wished to say anything. 'Oliver', in a firm voice, instantly and most distinctly replied, *"All I have to say is, to inform this congregation that I am a guilty man; the other is an innocent man. That is all I have to say."*

The cap was drawn over his face. The executioner took his station and at about 12.30 the offender was hanged. Having remained suspended for the usual time, the body was cut down, placed in the coffin and was buried within the precincts of the prison during the afternoon.

There followed much curious speculation over the significance of 'Buckingham Joe's' red handkerchief, dropped in view of the crowd. This was usually considered to be a sign from a condemned man that he hadn't betrayed another person. We may wonder who that person was, as he had already named 'Turpin' as Longley. The conclusion is that George Avery had put them up to the job, their reward being the money the farmer carried, Avery's reward being revenge. Alternatively, it was also argued that the fact he had a red handkerchief at all was pure chance as he'd sent Mrs Gardner, a turnkey's wife, out to buy two handkerchiefs – one just happened to be red, the other was striped muslin. These handkerchiefs had been bought and charged to his account long before the unfortunate man realised he would receive his punishment.

AUSTRALIA-BOUND

Galley received a second reprieve but was still transported to Australia. This action seemed beyond belief to most right thinking people – if the man was guilty, he should hang – if he was innocent he should go free. Galley wrote many times to the Home Office but was ignored. Over the next 42 years Galley campaigned for a pardon. He discovered that Longley was living in New South Wales and implored the authorities to arrest the man. Again, he was ignored. Eventually one of his letters appeared in the *Western Times* and was read by Lord Chief Justice Cockburn. He wrote to the Home Secretary, Mr R. A. Cross, and it took a whole year for him to receive a reply. No, he would not reopen the case.

By this time the sons of the original individuals who were taking an interest – the son of Mr Harvey, the solicitor, was one and the other, the son of Captain

Karslake, who had been one of the magistrates committing the men for trial in 1836. Karslake's widow, along with other now-elderly participants at the trial, petitioned for a pardon, even though she was over 80 years old. Letters came from all sorts of respectable people, chaplains, mayors, bishops, Members of Parliament. The Home Secretary remained unmoved. It wasn't until it was pointed out that he alone refused to reconsider the matter and that potentially he may have to resign over the issue, that he changed his mind. Finally, Galley, who had spent most of his life in Australia, returned to England where he collected £1000 compensation for serving time over a crime he did not commit.

MURDER
OR MISHAP?

T his final story may or may not have been a murder, but it certainly remains a mystery. Between Halwell and Dartmouth, on the B3207 road, is Woodlands Leisure Park, near Blackawton. Amongst its many attractions is the Monks Pool, surrounded by trees. This was the scene of a mysterious and unexplained death in April 1884, an intriguing story.

THE VICTIM

L aura Dimes was the 22 year-old daughter, the youngest of four children, of a barrister who owned the Oldstone estate at Blackawton. Oldstone was a somewhat gloomy place in which to grow up and as the Dimes were neither sociable nor well-to-do, Laura did not get to meet many eligible young men as she approached marriageable age. Her two sisters, though in a similar situation, had managed to marry, Ellen in 1879 and Matilda in 1881, leaving Laura at home, alone with her ageing parents and, of course, the staff.

Laura was nonetheless, a single-minded young lady and not a prisoner. She would visit her sisters and almost every day would go on long horse rides, with the local countryside proving wonderful for such equine excursions. Her favourite route took her from Oldstone to nearby Cotterbury, where her married sister, Matilda Shapley, lived. Laura sometimes visited before continuing across country to Bow,

onto Wollaton Cross before reaching the coast at Slapton Sands. Her return journey took her through Strete, in an age when there were still stagecoaches operating along the steep, twisting coast road. This open air freedom was further increased and enjoyed by the times she spent with her beloved collie, Juno, who enjoyed a scamper, particularly down to the ponds in the valley below Oldstone. Here Juno would plunge in with gay abandon, reveling in the cool waters and in blissful ignorance that her mistress would, one day soon, be found dead there.

SLAPTON SANDS

THE VILLAIN

Hugh Shortland came from a respectable family and appeared to have all the right credentials in an era when the number of eligible young ladies greatly outnumbered those of equally eligible young men. However, although he had the right connections there was something about his attitude and character that many were suspicious of, and as he was often short of money, he had to borrow to maintain his image. It was imperative for him to marry into money and as such, Laura would have been a suitable candidate.

It is believed that his first meeting with her, in one of those lanes where she rode, was stage-managed and not the chance meeting that she thought it was.

The scene was made more dramatic as the fateful meeting coincided with Laura entangling herself in some overhanging branches. The gallant young Shortland rushed to disentangle her and from that moment onwards, she fell for his charms.

Initially he was accepted as a regular visitor to Oldstone but as the relationship blossomed her parents must have heard about Shortland's reputation as being something of a gold digger. Determined that he wouldn't acquire such treasure by marrying their daughter, they forbade her to become engaged to him.

MARRIAGE & MYSTERY

Laura decided otherwise. She married Shortland without all the ceremony that would normally have accompanied such a wedding. In early April 1884, she became Mrs Hugh Shortland at the Kingsbridge Registry Office, having ridden there on horseback. After the simple ceremony Laura returned home to her parents. She planned to continue living there because Shortland was scheduled to go to New Zealand on business. Perhaps he would combine his trip to pay a visit to his father who lived there. This unfortunate timing may have caused the newlyweds not to consummate their marriage. It's also believed that Shortland would have liked to have kept the wedding a secret from Laura's parents, but she was not the deceitful kind. Although disapproving of her choice, they accepted the situation with apparent good grace.

In the immediate days after the wedding, Shortland visited his new wife at Oldstone, their days spent walking around the estate. Later, when asked if he had stayed the night, Mr Dimes is believed to have declined to answer. Shortland is supposed to have stayed at Mallet's Hotel at Ivybridge but if he did, then he had a long cross-country journey to see his new wife.

The visits came to an end when he bade her a farewell on Thursday 10th April 1884, before setting off for New Zealand. His last deed was to write to her from Ivybridge on the following Monday. Laura returned to the routine that had been part of her life for so long. She still had Juno who needed walking – and swimming – and the countryside remained as beautiful and the daily horse rides as pleasurable. However, all this came to a tragic end just two weeks after her husband's last letter to her. On Tuesday 29th April 1884, Laura's lifeless body was found floating upright in the upper pond. Her body was recovered with some difficulty by two local men, Luckraft and Langworthy. They placed her on a door, which had lain disused nearby, and carried her up to Oldstone.

The inquest was held the following day at Oldstone and local Dartmouth-based surgeon, Dr Soper, reported that he found only a few marks on Laura's face. He was of the opinion that there was little point in holding a post-mortem. The inquest recorded a verdict of death by drowning but noted that there was no evidence to explain how Laura entered the water. A letter, which had arrived on the morning that Laura's body had been found, was read out saying that her husband was getting on with his business as fast as he could, in order to return home as soon as possible.

In the wake of the tragedy there was an attempt to piece together Laura's last hours. It transpired that she had gone for her morning ride and had possibly been seen by a Mrs Hicks. She believed she saw Laura, on horseback, accompanied by two men, intent on preventing their identity from being known. They were certainly successful in this respect, as over a century later nobody seems to know who the mysterious accomplices were. It is claimed that Laura returned home at noon, to change from her riding habit into a blue day dress to take her dog out for a walk, probably down to the ponds. This latter aspect is claimed because no one actually saw her, and the strange part was that she broke with the dress code of the age by mixing her attire, choosing to continue wearing her riding hat and riding gloves. Surely, if she had to remove her gloves and hat to change her dress, it would have been simpler, and more in keeping with the time. For Laura to also pick up the matching bonnet and gloves? Suspicions were aroused.

The story took a dramatic twist when it was discovered that Hugh Shortland wasn't in New Zealand but was simply across the South Hams at Modbury. Those with a suspicious mind will automatically assume that 'here is our man' and that Laura met her not by misadventure but at the hands of a murderer. What else could anybody think? Questions must be asked as to why, with a loving new wife, would Shortland concoct and elaborate story about going to New Zealand, when in fact, he was visiting a friend's house for several weeks? His plans had been quite cleverly calculated, for all mail to Laura was sent in a box to his solicitor, who then passed the unfranked mail on to her, so there were no revealing post marks to show that he was half a world closer than New Zealand. Part of Hugh Shortland's childhood had been spent at Modbury, before emigrating to New Zealand with his father, and he still had friends there, most notably, William Thomas Ryder. Mrs Ryder, William's mother, broke the news to Shortland of his wife's death. Hugh was, apparently, devastated and, for his own good, they removed all sharp articles and razor blades so that he wouldn't be tempted to take his own life. He even went off his food, his appetite blunted by the tragedy.

The police made their enquiries throughout the district and questioned Mr Ryder senior, known to all who knew him as Modbury Bill, regarding the whereabouts of Shortland, who was actually in his house. The police discovered, from Modbury Bill, that the letter read out at the inquest had, in fact, been sent by him from Plymouth, not Brindisi, as had been thought. The police also questioned his son, William, who had often done as Shortland had asked. This included posting letters from 'abroad' to Laura. Whilst they interviewed him, Shortland was just yards away even though the police, at that time, thought he really was out of the country.

Shortland realised that if he maintained his concealment and carried on with the pretence with the letters, it could be construed as an admission of his guilt for having murdered his young bride. To prove his innocence, he had to come out of hiding and the first step he took was to dispatch his friend, William Ryder, to Plymouth to contact his solicitor, Mr E. G. Bennet. He would, in all probability, have some work to do for Shortland in the ensuing months. He also instructed Ryder to have some flowers sent to be placed on Laura's grave.

Laura's brother travelled from London to Devon. He had suspected that there was something awry with the situation and was determined to get to the bottom of the matter. Intuition, and perhaps a few whispers, took him to Modbury where he called on the Ryder household. He heard footsteps from within but nobody answered the door. The next day, the police called at the house and Shortland was arrested. As was to be expected, he protested his innocence but, nevertheless, he was escorted the short distance, less than a quarter of a mile, to Modbury's police station. Shackled by handcuffs, Shortland was later taken in an open trap to Kingsbridge. Here the magistrate read the charge that Hugh Rotherford Shortland *"...did feloniously, wilfully and of malice aforethought, kill and murder one Laura Shortland"*.

He was remanded in custody whilst evidence was gathered to prove, one way or another, whether he was guilty of such a terrible crime. An application was made to the Home Secretary to exhume Laura's body, so that it would be possible to determine if she was dead before going into the pond or whether she had drowned, as had been originally thought. The case for the prosecution would be greater with more evidence and a lot of groundwork followed in the search for the truth. Personnel from Scotland Yard came to Devon looking for clues to reveal the cause of Laura's fate.

Meanwhile Shortland proclaimed, vehemently, that his alibi was that he had been at the Ryder's house all the time. This, though, was disproved for there were various witnesses to testify that he had been seen all over the district in that fateful month of April.

William Ryder was coaxed back to Modbury, from Plymouth, and was immediately treated to the same open trap journey to Kingsbridge. Once there, he was charged with aiding and abetting Shortland in Laura's murder. However, the bench dismissed the case against Ryder's participation, particularly in relation to the letter-posting incident, as there was insufficient involvement to seek committal. It is inevitable that in cases like this imaginative theories abound. It was suggested that Laura may have been poisoned by substances that wouldn't have been detected in 1884. The pond was drained on 13 May, partly in the expectation that an empty poison bottle would be found. It wasn't.

The next day, the gruesome task of exhuming and examining Laura's corpse was completed in a single day, so that she was laid to rest again before the sun went down. However, many of her internal organs were removed and sent to Dr du Pré of Westminster Hospital in London for analysis. The post-mortem took several hours and was a thorough examination. Her head was also given great consideration for it was believed that it might provide vital clues.

THE HUSBAND STANDS TRIAL

The trial was arranged for Kingsbridge Town Hall on 15th May 1884, and as the case had been the talk of the entire district, great crowds had gathered to see the outcome. However, a postponement was requested because the results of the analysis of Laura's body contents had not yet arrived. A similar situation was re-enacted on 23rd May, thereby frustrating Hugh Shortland who wanted his freedom. After another week had passed all the relevant parties were pitched together on Saturday 31st May, to sort the matter out, at least in the eyes of the law.

The Crown was represented by Chief Inspector Roots and Mr William Golden, who was one of the solicitors of the Treasury and a key figure on this occasion. In his statement he spelled out that an exhaustive inquiry had been made into Laura's death. The results of the investigation were such that the suspicions about Shortland had been removed. He went on to say that Shortland had, by his actions, put himself into the situation that he found himself in. He concluded, on behalf of the Crown, that the charges would be dropped and his comments were met with spontaneous applause from those who had come to see the result. Shortland was a man who had had a mighty burden lifted from his shoulders and his relief was all too plain to see. Shortland was so convinced of his own innocence, and angry at the injustice he felt for being held on remand, that had they tried to hold him any longer, he would have issued summonses against the whole Bench and Superintendent Dore! On leaving the court the first thing he did was to go along the road to the King's Arms and have a drink with his solicitor.

That should have been the end of it but there were a few postscripts that only serve to make one even more curious about this sad and sorry affair.

Hugh Shortland's trial goes against the grain of most murder cases. No witnesses were ever present to confirm, deny or simply look mystified at the questions asked of them. Hugh Shortland was never interrogated in front of the public's gaze or made to account for his bizarre behaviour. His own solicitor's attempts to speak or ask questions were virtually quashed each time he tried. But, most strange of all, was the fact that the results of the post-mortem were not revealed.

It was believed that Laura's body did not show the classic signs of death by drowning as it had floated to the surface far too soon, suggesting that there was air in her lungs. Had she drowned there would have been other indicators, such as the way her face would have been at the moment of death following a frantic struggle to survive. In all probability Laura was dead before reaching the water. The questions remains – what was found during the post-mortem which resulted in the termination by the prosecution?

POND ON DARTMOOR

THE HUSBAND CRIES 'MURDER'

Hugh Shortland campaigned vigorously to turn the wheels of justice so that he could have the satisfaction of seeing his wife's killers put on trial. He was utterly convinced that she had been murdered and could not believe that she had fallen in the pond whilst playing with her dog. It was also too much for him to accept that she had committed suicide; she was not the type of person to do that. Shortland put forward his theory that Laura had been poisoned by an evanescent substance, one that vanishes, which would not have been recognised by pathologists in that era. Research also showed that his father was something of an expert on aborigines and was conversant with the sort of poisons that could be extracted from plants in that part of the southern hemisphere. Had Hugh inherited some of his father's knowledge? However, this leads to a further question of who would have had a motive for the only person to financially gain from losing Laura was himself. So why draw attention to the possibilities? Unless of course he had committed 'the perfect murder' and wanted it acknowledged as such.

REPEAT PRESCRIPTION?

Perhaps the answer lies in Hugh Shortland's future actions...Hugh did eventually make that journey across the world, for it is documented that in 1891 he had another brush with the law, this time in New Zealand. The case proved just how low he was prepared to stoop and how 'dirty' he was prepared to play. Shortland had resumed his career as a solicitor and in the course of his work a young lady called at his office on behalf of her mother. Shortland clearly earmarked the girl as a potential wife, and her mother asked a local priest to investigate Shortland's character. She didn't like what she learned. One day, finding himself 'short of funds', Shortland called on the mother and received a very frosty reception. She told Shortland that she would never allow a marriage between her daughter and him. Shortland lost his temper and said that if he couldn't have her, he'd see to it that no one else would! A struggle involving a poker ensued and Shortland was ejected from the house.

Following this humiliation, Shortland put a plan into action and started following the girl. When he saw her go to a circus with a male friend, he rushed back to the mother's house to cast a slur on her character. The young lady returned to the house and was clearly shocked that her mother might believe Shortland over her word and swept out of the house. Shortland followed her and reported back that she was headed for the wharf, causing the mother to fear for her daughter's life. Luckily, the girl's brother stepped in to stop her.

Shortland started to spread the word that the young girl was of 'loose morals' and soon found himself in court facing libel charges. Fortunately for her, there were two doctors who, after examining her, were prepared to confirm her chastity. But even then, Shortland argued the point that doctors could make a mistake and in a criminal case their evidence would not be admissible. He stated that the girl had accused him of murdering his first wife because she was jealous that he had recently married.

It took the jury all of ten minutes to find Shortland 'guilty'. Although he had some of the 'stuffing knocked out of him' by the verdict, he still managed to try to influence the Judge over his sentencing, suggesting that it was his first offence after all. Unluckily for him, the Judge was not so easily swayed by his charms and even suggested that he'd have liked the power to add a few lashes to the two years' imprisonment to which he was sentencing him!

Besides being a blackguard, Hugh Shortland was clearly a conman and an opportunist. Before he married Laura, he had several schemes in the pipeline in which he wished the public to invest. His purpose in 'going to New Zealand' was probably to convince people that he was a well-travelled businessman. Sending letters to Laura keeping her informed of his movements would have added to his authenticity. It has sometimes been suggested that Laura discovered his dubious activities and refused to give him money, but the girl was in love with her new husband. A man as charming as he would surely have spent time encouraging her trust in him. However, there appears no motive at this stage in their relationship to believe he would want her dead.

One of the puzzling facts of both Laura's situation and the young lady in New Zealand, is that the virtue of both girls remained intact. It is particularly odd that he never consummated his marriage, and if he was prepared to go to court to slur a girl's reputation, why didn't he back up his words with actions? One might almost think Shortland had behaved 'like a gentleman' but by all accounts, he was far removed from that status. The Judge in Auckland referred to Shortland as being *"debased and destitute of every spark of honour which should be innate in every man"*. If we take this a step further, we can see why the parents involved would be so vehement in their desire to protect their innocent daughters! Our antipodean mother was clearly made of strong stuff and succeeded in her protection, but the quiet, sheltered lifestyle of the Dimes did not nurture the same fighting spirit.

GUILTY CONSCIENCE?

O r did it? Perhaps in the logic of the Victorian parents, their 'precious' daughter was better dead than defiled. It was particularly important that she should not have committed suicide as the repercussions for her body and soul were too great. Supposing a third party had been employed to put her beyond the reaches of her husband? That would account for her mother's strange behaviour in not searching for Laura when she failed to arrive home. When the police first inspected the body, they noted that there was nothing about her clothing to suggest she'd been attacked or robbed. But that assumes she had been attacked after she'd changed her clothes…nobody saw who collected a fresh dress, they merely said they heard her come in, change and go out again. Did anyone ever ask to see the state of the discarded riding habit in her room? And would her mother have allowed them access, or would she have declared it irrelevant? In any case, bearing in mind that murder was not considered a possibility until Shortland was discovered in hiding, there was plenty of time to repair or destroy the clothes.

It was reported that the parents were certain that Shortland had nothing to do with her death. Surely, he should have been their prime suspect? Why did Mr Dimes decline to answer questions about Shortland's visits to the house? Had he perhaps come to an arrangement with his son-in-law that they would say nothing to the community of his dubious business activities provided he never laid a finger on their daughter? If Laura met with an 'accident' it would also account for Hugh Shortland's reaction on learning of his wife's death and his attempts to keep the case open after he had personally been cleared.

Despite having three other children, plus grandchildren, to live for, we are told that the sad loss of her youngest daughter proved too much for Mrs Dimes; she pined away from a broken heart, just one year later, almost to the day.

Coincidentally, Mr Dimes also died in April but that was a few years later in 1891, just as the Great Blizzard was gripping the South Hams in a deep freeze that caused immense disruption. Just four years later, on Saturday 16th February 1895, things became suddenly much hotter at Oldstone when the old mansion succumbed to a blaze, which razed it to the ground. Today, it is said that the pond has a ghost but whether or not it is Laura is not known; she is probably the only one who knows for sure what really happened that Spring day all those years ago.

And here our tales must end. Whether murder or mystery is hard to confirm and is now for the reader to decide. There are many tales of strange and unusual events in Devon, particularly on Dartmoor. Take at look at Tor Mark's other books to find out more.